My Mane
Catches the Wind

POEMS ABOUT HORSES

SELECTED BY
Lee Bennett Hopkins

ILLUSTRATED BY
Sam Savitt

My Mane Catches

the Wind

Harcourt Brace Jovanovich   New York and London

Every effort has been made to trace the ownership of all copyrighted material and to secure the necessary permissions to reprint these selections. In the event of any question arising as to the use of any material, the editor and the publisher, while expressing regret for any inadvertent error, will be happy to make the necessary correction in future printings.

Thanks are due to the following for permission to reprint the copyrighted materials listed below:

ATHENEUM PUBLISHERS, INC., for "Little Horse" from *The Carrier of Ladders* by W. S. Merwin. Copyright © 1969, 1970 by W. S. Merwin.

THOMAS Y. CROWELL for "Horses" from *Feathered Ones and Furry* by Aileen Fisher. Copyright © 1971 by Aileen Fisher.

HARPER & ROW, PUBLISHERS, INC., for "The Horses" from *Up Country: Poems of New England* by Maxine Kumin. Copyright © 1972 by Maxine Kumin; and for an excerpt from "For a Shetland Pony Brood Mare Who Died in Her Barren Year" from *Up Country: Poems of New England* by Maxine Kumin. Copyright © 1970 by Maxine Kumin.

WILLIAM HEINEMANN LTD. for "The Four Horses" and "The Grey Horse" from *The Wandering Moon* by James Reeves.

HOLT, RINEHART AND WINSTON for "The Runaway" from *The Poetry of Robert Frost* edited by Edward Connery Lathem. Copyright 1923, © 1969 by Holt, Rinehart and Winston. Copyright 1951 by Robert Frost.

BERTHA KLAUSNER INTERNATIONAL LITERARY AGENCY, INC., for "A Horse Is a Horse" by Dorothy W. Baruch from *I Would Like to Be a Pony.*

ALFRED A. KNOPF, INC., for "One day . . ." by Wilford Horne, Jr., from *City Talk* compiled by Lee Bennett Hopkins. Copyright © 1970 by Lee Bennett Hopkins.

J. B. LIPPINCOTT COMPANY for "White Horses," Copyright 1933, © renewed 1961 by Eleanor Farjeon, from *Poems for Children* by Eleanor Farjeon. Copyright 1951 by Eleanor Farjeon.

MACMILLAN, LONDON AND BASINGSTOKE, for "The Prayer of the Foal" and "The Prayer of the Old Horse" from *Prayers from the Ark* by Carmen Bernos de Gasztold, translated by Rumer Godden.

JAMES N. MILLER for "Foal" from *Menagerie* by Mary Britton Miller.

NEW DIRECTIONS PUBLISHING CORPORATION for "The Horse" by William Carlos Williams from *The Collected Later Poems.* Copyright 1948 by William Carlos Williams.

W. W. NORTON & COMPANY, INC., for "Horse" from *Plain Song,* Poems, by James Harrison. Copyright © 1965 by James Harrison.

HAROLD OBER ASSOCIATES, INC., for "White Horses" from *Poems for Children* by Eleanor Farjeon. Copyright © 1933, 1961 by Eleanor Farjeon.

PENGUIN BOOKS LTD. for "Birth of the Foal" by Ferenc Juhász, translated by David Wevill, from *Sándor Weöres and Ferenc Juhász: Selected Poems* (Penguin Modern European Poets, 1970), © Ferenc Juhász, 1970, translation © David Wevill, 1970.

PRINCE REDCLOUD for "Anywhere." Used by permission of the author who controls all rights.

SMITHSONIAN INSTITUTION PRESS for a selection from "Teton Sioux Music" by Frances Densmore; Song No. 108, page 299, from *Smithsonian Institution Bureau of American Ethnology,* Bulletin 61. Washington, D.C.: Government Printing Office, 1918.

UNIVERSITY OF CALIFORNIA PRESS for four lines from *Issa: The Year of My Life,* translated by Nobuyuki Yuasa. Copyright 1960, 1972 by The Regents of the University of California.

THE VIKING PRESS and VIKING PENGUIN INC. for "Horse" from *Under the Tree* by Elizabeth Madox Roberts. Copyright 1922 by B. W. Huebsch, Inc. Copyright © 1950 by Ivor S. Roberts; and for "The Prayer of the Foal" and "The Prayer of the Old Horse" from *Prayers from the Ark* by Carmen Bernos de Gasztold and translated by Rumer Godden. Copyright © 1962 by Rumer Godden.

Special thanks to the Viking Press and Viking Penguin Inc. and to Macmillan, London and Basingstoke, for use of the title from "The Prayer of the Foal" by Carmen Bernos de Gasztold, translated by Rumer Godden.

LIBRARY OF CONGRESS CATALOGING IN PUBLICATION DATA

Main entry under title: My mane catches the wind.

Includes index.
SUMMARY: A collection of 22 poems about horses.
1. Horses—Juvenile poetry.   2. Children's poetry.
[1. Horses—Poetry.   2. Poetry—Collections]
I. Hopkins, Lee Bennett.   II. Savitt, Sam.
PN6110.H7M9   808.81'9'36   79–87518
ISBN 0–15–256343–1

First edition

B C D E

Contents

Introduction

Poets sing of everything.

In this book of poems, you will meet poets who have sung in praise of horses young and old—foals, colts, dapples, greys, Shetlands, Morgans, the quarter horse, the stallion, the cart horse.

Horses, friend and servant of humankind for centuries unrecorded, have inspired poets from England, Hungary, Japan, France, and rural and urban America to pay tribute to one of the most beloved animals on earth.

Come. Meet the magnificent horses in *My Mane Catches the Wind.*

Lee Bennett Hopkins
Scarborough, New York

My Mane Catches the Wind

Birth of the Foal

FERENC JUHÁSZ

As May was opening the rosebuds,
elder and lilac beginning to bloom,
it was time for the mare to foal.
She'd rest herself, or hobble lazily

after the boy who sang as he led her
to pasture, wading through the meadowflowers.
They wandered back at dusk, bone-tired,
the moon perched on a blue shoulder of sky.

Then the mare lay down,
sweating and trembling, on her straw in the stable.
The drowsy, heavy-bellied cows
surrounded her, waiting, watching, snuffing.

Later, when even the hay slept
and the shaft of the Plow pointed south,
the foal was born. Hours the mare
spent licking the foal with its glue-blind eyes.

And the foal slept at her side,
a heap of feathers ripped from a bed.
Straw never spread as soft as this.
Milk or snow never slept like a foal.

Dawn bounced up in a bright red hat,
waved at the world and skipped away.
Up staggered the foal,
its hooves were jelly-knots of foam.

Then day sniffed with its blue nose
through the open stable window, and found them—
the foal nuzzling its mother,
velvet fumbling for her milk.

Then all the trees were talking at once,
chickens scrabbled in the yard,
like golden flowers
envy withered the last stars.

ISSA

Step aside, step aside,
Little sparrows.
His lordship, Sir Horse,
Is coming through.

Foal

MARY BRITTON MILLER

Come trotting up
Beside your mother,
Little skinny.

Lay your neck across
Her back, and whinny,
Little foal.

You think you're a horse
Because you can trot—
But you're not.

Your eyes are so wild,
And each leg is as tall
As a pole;

And you're only a skittish
Child, after all,
Little foal.

The Prayer of the Foal
CARMEN BERNOS DE GASZTOLD

O God! the grass is so young!
My hooves are full of capers.
Then
why does this terror start up in me?
I race
and my mane catches the wind.
I race
and Your scents beat on my heart.
I race,
falling over my own feet in my joy,
because my eyes are too big
and I am their prisoner:
eyes too quick to seize
on the uneasiness that runs through the whole world.
Dear God,
when the strange night
prowls round the edge of day,
let Yourself be moved by my plaintive whinny;
set a star to watch over me
and hush my fear.

                                        Amen

Little Horse

W. S. MERWIN

You come from some other forest
do you
little horse
think how long I have known these
deep dead leaves
without meeting you

I belong to no one
I would have wished for you if I had known how
what a long time the place was empty
even in my sleep
and loving it as I did
I could not have told what was missing

what can I show you
I will not ask you if you will stay
or if you will come again
I will not try to hold you
I hope you will come with me to where I stand
often sleeping and waking
by the patient water
that has no father nor mother

The Horse
WILLIAM CARLOS WILLIAMS

The horse moves
independently
without reference
to his load

He has eyes
like a woman and
turns them
about, throws

back his ears
and is generally
conscious of
the world. Yet

he pulls when
he must and
pulls well, blowing
fog from

his nostrils
like fumes from
the twin
exhausts of a car.

from *Song of Myself*
WALT WHITMAN

A gigantic beauty of a stallion, fresh and responsive to my caresses,
Head high in the forehead and wide between the ears,
Limbs glossy and supple, tail dusting the ground,
Eyes well apart and full of sparkling wickedness. . . . ears finely cut
    and flexibly moving.

His nostrils dilate. . . . my heels embrace him. . . . his well-built limbs
    tremble with pleasure. . . . we speed around and return.

I but use you a moment and then I resign you stallion. . . . and do
    not need your paces, and outgallop them,
And myself as I stand or sit pass faster than you.

Horse

ELIZABETH MADOX ROBERTS

His bridle hung around the post;
The sun and the leaves made spots come down;
I looked close at him through the fence;
The post was drab and he was brown.

His nose was long and hard and still,
And on his lip were specks like chalk.
But once he opened up his eyes,
And he began to talk.

He didn't talk out with his mouth;
He didn't talk with words or noise.
The talk was there along his nose;
It seemed and then it was.

He said the day was hot and slow,
And he said he didn't like the flies;
They made him have to shake his skin,
And they got drowned in his eyes.

He said that drab was just about
The same as brown, but he was not
A post, he said, to hold a fence.
"I'm horse," he said, "that's what!"

And then he shut his eyes again.
As still as they had been before.
He said for me to run along
And not to bother him any more.

The Grey Horse

JAMES REEVES

A dappled horse stood at the edge of the meadow,
He was peaceful and quiet and grey as a shadow.
Something he seemed to be saying to me,
As he stood in the shade of the chestnut tree.

'It's a wonderful morning,' he seemed to say,
'So jump on my back, and let's be away!
It's over the hedge we'll leap and fly,
And up the hill to the edge of the sky.

'For over the hill there are fields without end;
On the galloping downs we can run like the wind.
Down pathways we'll canter, by streams we'll stray,
Oh, jump on my back and let's be away!'

As I went by the meadow one fine summer morn,
The grey horse had gone like a ghost with the dawn;
He had gone like a ghost and not waited for me,
And it's over the hilltop he'd surely be.

Horse

JIM HARRISON

A
quarter horse, no rider
canters through the pasture

thistles raise soft purple burrs
her flanks are shiny in the sun

I whistle and she runs
almost sideways toward me

the oats in my hand are sweets to her:

dun mane furling in its breeze,
her neck
corseted with muscle,
wet teeth friendly against my hand—
how can I believe
you ran under a low maple limb
to knock me off?

White Horses
ELEANOR FARJEON

Count the white horses you meet on the way,
Count the white horses, child, day after day,
Keep a wish ready for wishing—if you
Wish on the ninth horse, your wish will come true.

I saw a white horse at the end of the lane,
I saw a white horse canter down by the shore,
I saw a white horse that was drawing a wain,
And one drinking out of a trough: that made four.

I saw a white horse gallop over the down,
I saw a white horse looking over a gate,
I saw a white horse on the way into town,
And one on the way coming back: that made eight.

But oh for the ninth one: where *he* tossed his mane,
And cantered and galloped and whinnied and swished
His silky white tail, I went looking in vain,
And the wish I had ready could never be wished.

Count the white horses you meet on the way,
Count the white horses, child, day after day,
Keep a wish ready for wishing—if you
Wish on the ninth horse, your wish will come true.

TETON SIOUX

Friend,
My horse
Flies like a bird
As it runs.

A Horse Is a Horse

DOROTHY W. BARUCH

I would like to be
A horse wild and free
Galloping with flying mane
Over miles of wide field,
Leaping fences and walls,
With the whistle of wind-sound
So strong in my ears
   That I
   Can simply not
   Certainly
   Not possibly
   Hear
       When anyone
         Calls.

WILFORD HORNE, JR.

One day
A horse ran fast
He ran so fast that wind,
Sunlight, and all the blue of day
Flew gone!

Horses

AILEEN FISHER

Standing up for sleeping
the way they do,
horses must be just as tired
after sleeping's through.

The Horses

MAXINE KUMIN

It has turned to snow in the night.
The horses have put on
their long fur stockings
and they are wearing
fur capes with high necks
out of which the device
of their ears makes four statues.
Their tails have caught flecks
of snow and hang down
loose as bedsheets.
They stand nose to nose
in the blue light that coats
the field before sunup
and rub dry their old kisses.

Anywhere

PRINCE REDCLOUD

On the

      white
      snow-topped
      hill

nearby
a white horse stood
midst eight reindeer.

A beautiful sight—
      such brown
      such white

on the

      white
      snow-topped
      hill

nearby.

The Runaway

ROBERT FROST

Once when the snow of the year was beginning to fall,
We stopped by a mountain pasture to say, "Whose colt?"
A little Morgan had one forefoot on the wall,
The other curled at his breast. He dipped his head
And snorted at us. And then he had to bolt.
We heard the miniature thunder where he fled,
And we saw him, or thought we saw him, dim and gray,
Like a shadow against the curtain of falling flakes.
"I think the little fellow's afraid of the snow.
He isn't winter-broken. It isn't play
With the little fellow at all. He's running away.
I doubt if even his mother could tell him, 'Sakes,
It's only weather.' He'd think she didn't know!
Where is his mother? He can't be out alone."
And now he comes again with clatter of stone,
And mounts the wall again with whited eyes
And all his tail that isn't hair up straight.
He shudders his coat as if to throw off flies.
"Whoever it is that leaves him out so late,
When other creatures have gone to stall and bin,
Ought to be told to come and take him in."

The Four Horses

JAMES REEVES

White Rose is a quiet horse
 For a lady to ride,
Jog-trotting on the high road
 Or through the countryside.

Grey Wolf is a hunter
 All muscle and fire;
Day long he will gallop
 And not tumble or tire.

Black Magic's a race-horse;
 She is gone like a ghost,
With the wind in her mane
 To whirl past the post.

But munching his fill
 In a field of green clover
Stands Brownie the cart-horse,
 Whose labor is over.

The Prayer of the Old Horse

CARMEN BERNOS DE GASZTOLD

See, Lord,
my coat hangs in tatters,
like homespun, old, threadbare.
All that I had of zest,
all my strength,
I have given in hard work
and kept nothing back for myself.
Now
my poor head swings
to offer up all the loneliness of my heart.
Dear God,
stiff on my thickened legs
I stand here before You:
Your unprofitable servant.
Oh! of Your goodness,
give me a gentle death.

Amen

from *For a Shetland Pony
Brood Mare Who Died
in Her Barren Year*

MAXINE KUMIN

. . .
you lay down and died
in the sun,
all silken on one side,
all mud on the other one.

from *Venus and Adonis*
WILLIAM SHAKESPEARE

And whether he run or fly they know not whether;
    For through his mane and tail the high wind sings,
    Fanning the hairs, who wave like feathered wings.

Index of Authors, Titles, and First Lines

Lee Bennett Hopkins is a well-known editor, writer, teacher, and consultant. He has hosted a public television series for children, the successful "Zebra Wings," which is shown nationwide. His articles have appeared in *Horn Book, Language Arts,* and *Learning.* His feature column, "Book Bonanza," appears monthly in *Teacher* magazine. He has compiled six volumes in the very popular holiday poetry series: *Hey-How for Halloween!; Sing Hey for Christmas Day!; Good Morning to You, Valentine; Beat the Drum; Merrily Comes Our Harvest In;* and *Easter Buds Are Springing.* In addition, he and John Earl, the photographer, have won praise for *To Look at Any Thing,* a combination of poetry and nature photographs. His novels *Mama* and *Wonder Wheels* have received wide critical acclaim. He lives in Westchester County, New York.

Sam Savitt and horses have been inseparable practically all of his life. He was born in Wilkes-Barre, Pennsylvania, and spent his summers hitch-hiking and working on ranches throughout the Southwest. Though he never had a horse of his own as a child, he managed to find and ride them everywhere he went—all the way from the milkman's horse in Wilkes-Barre to remounts in Burma, where he served with the army engineers during World War II. After the war he studied at the Art Students League and pursued his interest in horses. His ability as a horseman eventually led him into training hunters and jumpers—his star pupil made the United States Equestrian Team. He has written and illustrated fourteen books about horses in all fields, from rodeo to the Maryland Hunt Cup race. His illustrations have appeared in many national magazines, and he has illustrated over a hundred books by other authors. His paintings and drawings of horses hang in homes all over the country, and his horse charts are well known throughout the equestrian world. He is the official artist for the United States Equestrian Team.